Soothing
Patterns

igloobooks

igloobooks

Published in 2018
by Igloo Books Ltd
Cottage Farm
Sywell
NN6 0BJ
www.igloobooks.com

VIV001 1018
8 10 11 9 7
ISBN: 978-1-78557-420-7

Designed by Charles Wood-Penn
Edited by Vicky Taylor

Interiors illustrated by Angelika Scudamore
All other images: iStock

Printed and manufactured in Malaysia

Soothing Patterns

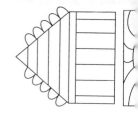
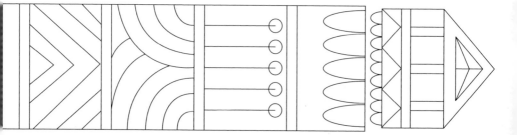
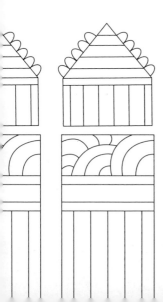

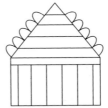

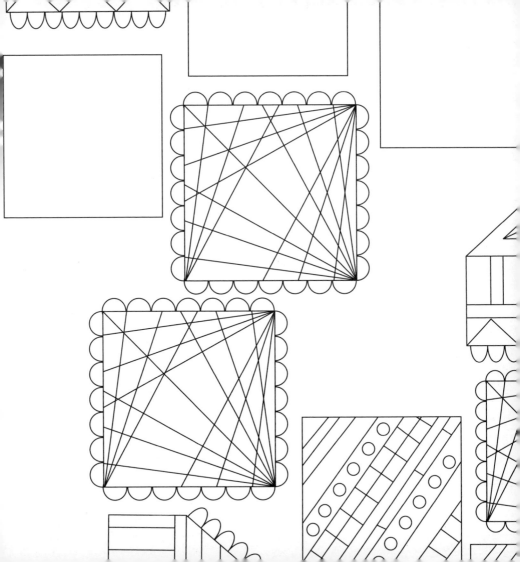

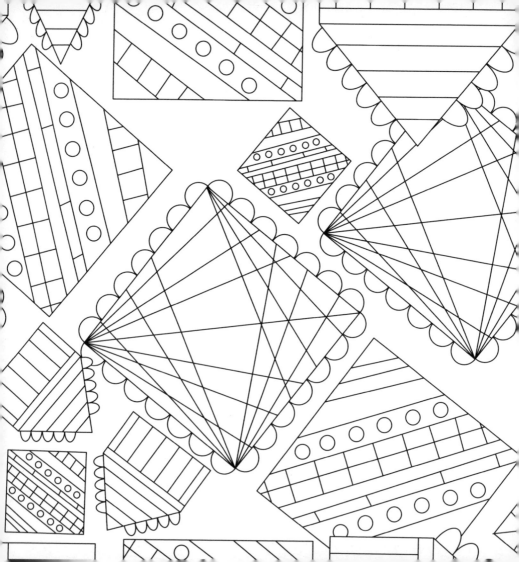

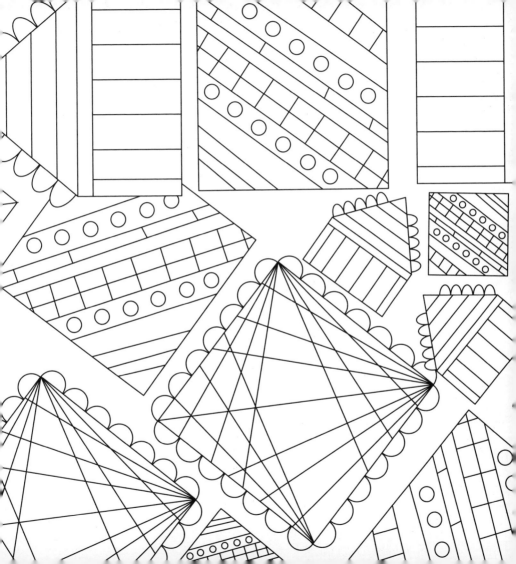

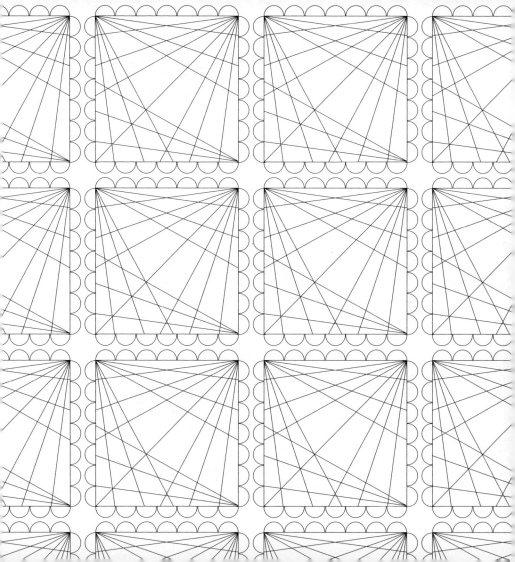

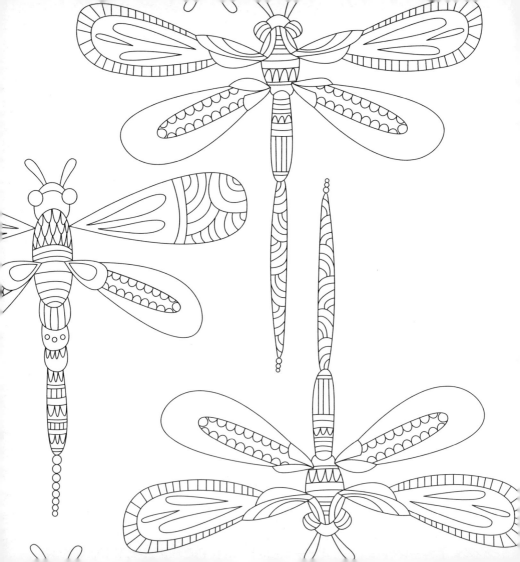

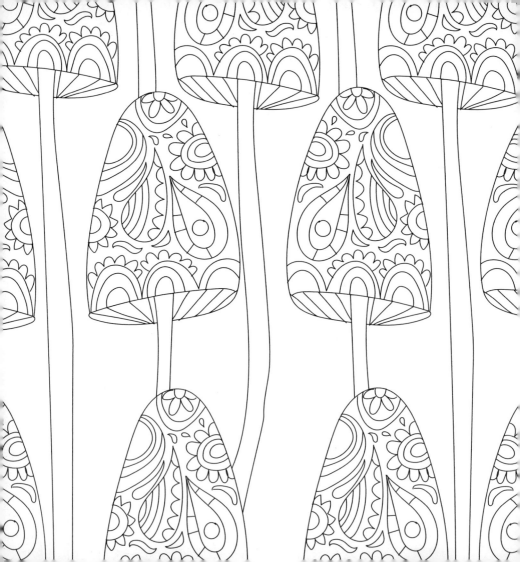

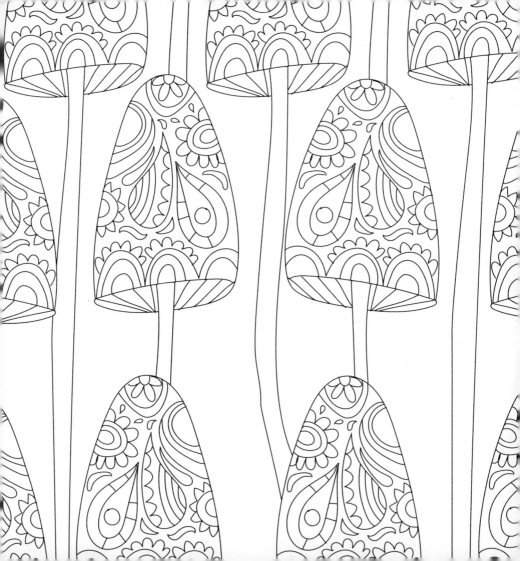

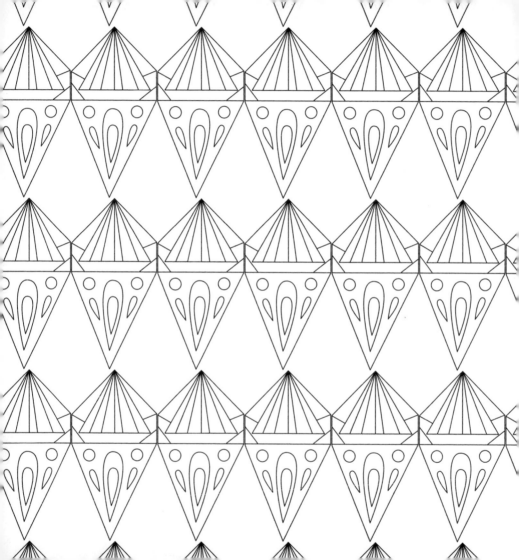